The Gospel Train

20 gospels & spirituals for solo voice or choir
with piano accompaniment and chord symbols.
Arranged by Peter Skellern.

Chester Music
(A division of Music Sales Limited)
8/9 Frith Street
London W1D 3JB

This book © Copyright 2001 Chester Music
Order No. CH61671 ISBN 0-7119-8586-3

Music processed by Olivia Kilmartin

Cover design by Chloe Alexander
Cover photograph by Jim Mathews
Printed in the United Kingdom by
Caligraving Limited, Thetford, Norfolk

Unauthorised reproduction of any part of this publication by any means
including photocopying is an infringement of copyright

Contents

The Gospel Train

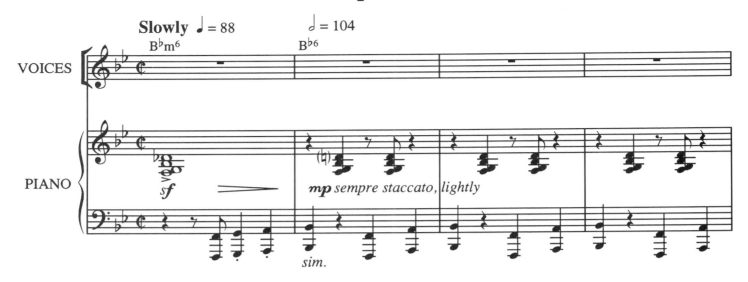

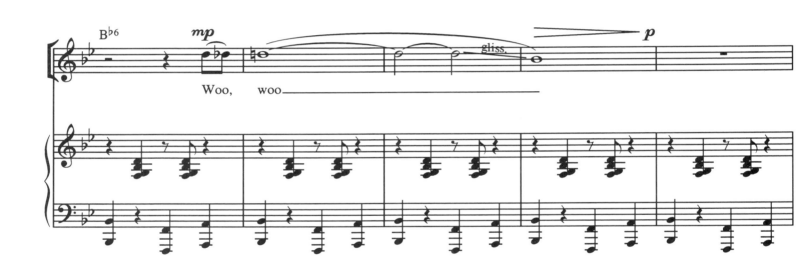

Woo,   woo

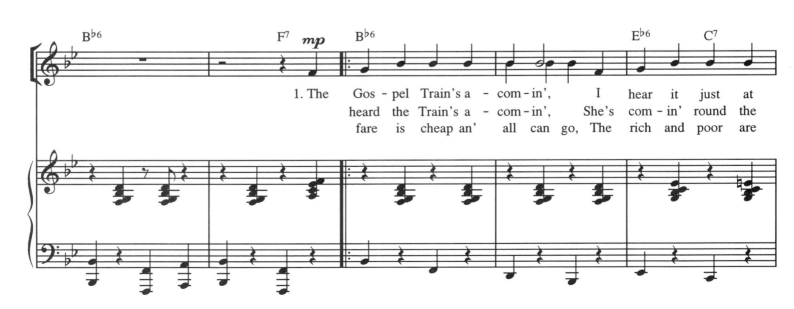

1. The Gos - pel Train's a - com - in',   I   hear it just   at
heard the Train's a - com - in', She's com - in' round the
fare is cheap an'   all can go, The   rich and poor are

This arrangement © Copyright 2000 Chester Music Limited

Joshua Fight De Battle Of Jericho

This arrangement © Copyright 2000 Chester Music Limited

Amazing Grace

The melody used here is the original one and is, in my opinion,
superior to the version we normally hear today.
Verses 1 & 2: unison (solo or small group)
Verse 3: harmonized (full choir). Verse 4: unison

This arrangement © Copyright 2000 Chester Music Limited

Go Down, Moses

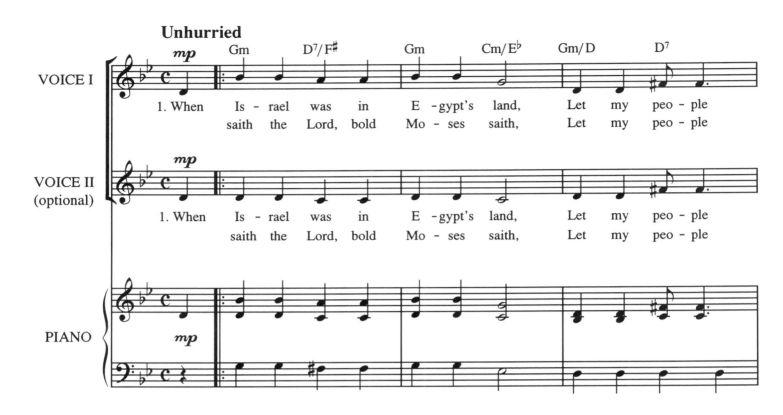

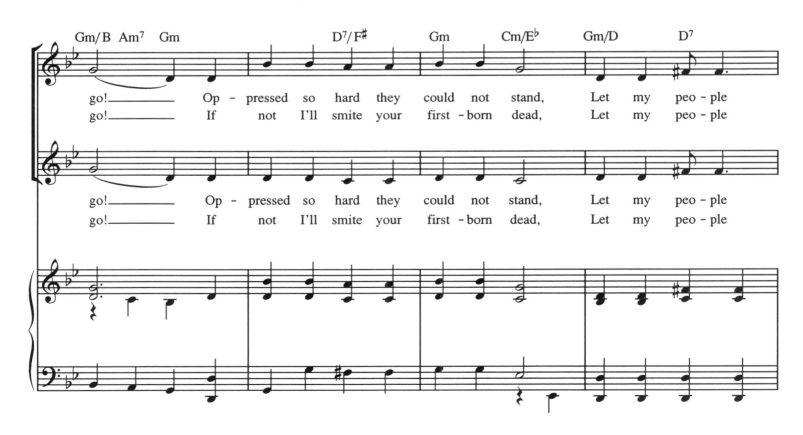

This arrangement © Copyright 2000 Chester Music Limited

Balm In Gilead

* Descant to be sung second and third time round only.

This arrangement © Copyright 2000 Chester Music Limited

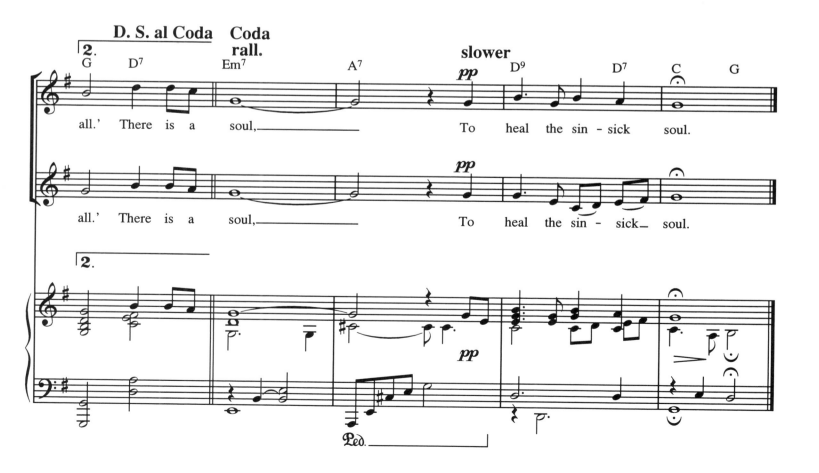

Good News!

This arrangement © Copyright 2000 Chester Music Limited

Deep River

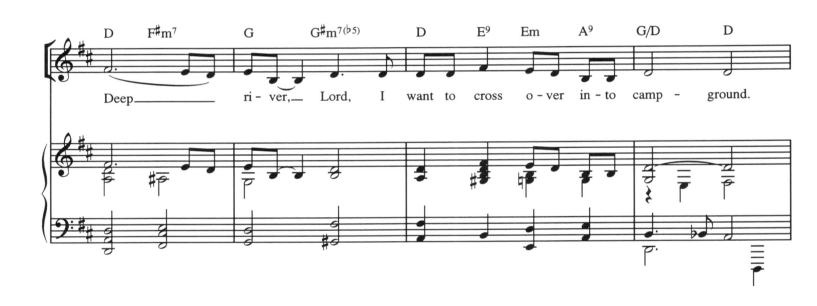

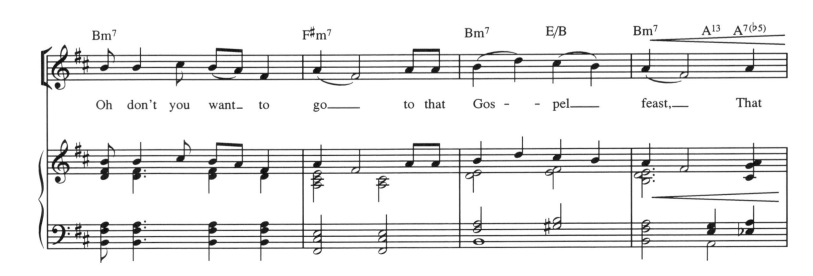

This arrangement © Copyright 2000 Chester Music Limited

pro - - mised land___ where all___ is peace.___ Deep___

ri - ver, my home is o - ver Jor - dan,___ Deep___

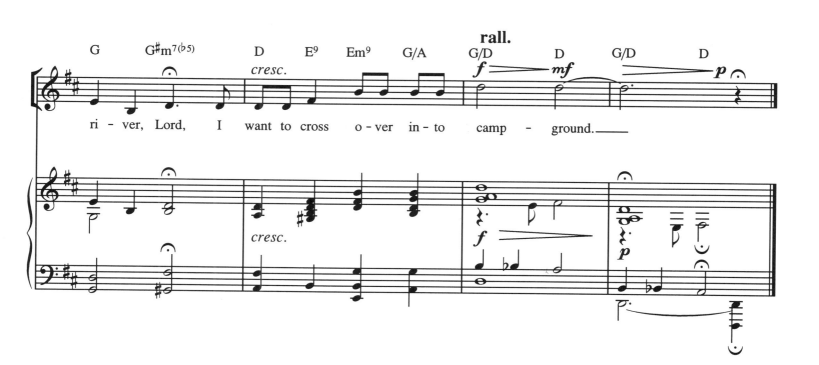

ri - ver, Lord, I want to cross o - ver in - to camp - ground.___

Didn't My Lord Deliver Daniel?

This arrangement © Copyright 2000 Chester Music Limited

Nobody Knows De Trouble I See

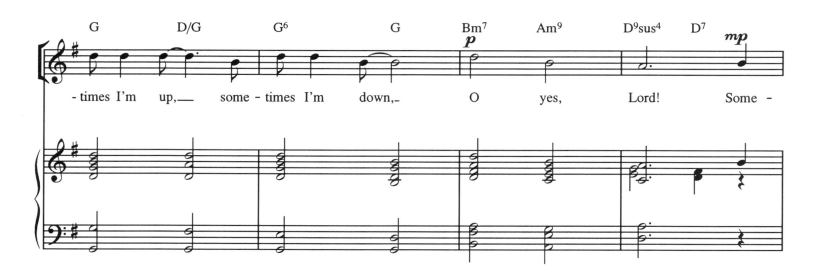

This arrangement © Copyright 2000 Chester Music Limited

The Gospel Train

20 gospels & spirituals for solo voice or choir.
Arranged by Peter Skellern.

vocal part

This vocal part may be photocopied.

Chester Music
(A division of Music Sales Limited)
8/9 Frith Street
London W1D 3JB

Contents

The Gospel Train

Woo,— woo———————

1. The Gos-pel Train's a-com-in', I hear it just at hand,—
heard the Train's a-com-in', She's com-in' round the curve,— She's
fare is cheap an' all can go, The rich and poor are there,— No

Hear the car wheel rum-blin' And rol-lin' thro the land.
loos-en'd all her steam and brakes, And strain-in' e-v'ry nerve.
se-cond class a-board this train, No dif-f'rence in the fare.
Git on board, lit-tle

chil-dren, git on board, lit-tle chil-dren, git on board, lit-tle chil-dren, there's

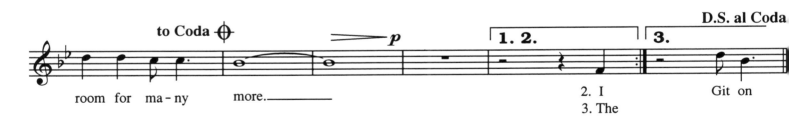

room for ma-ny more.———————
2. I
3. The
Git on

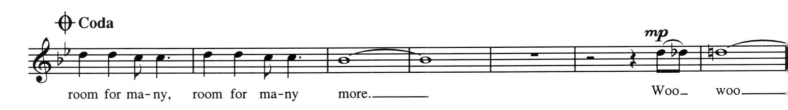

room for ma-ny, room for ma-ny more.———————
Woo— woo———

Pshhhhhhh

This arrangement © Copyright 2000 Chester Music Limited

Joshua Fight De Battle Of Jericho

This arrangement © Copyright 2000 Chester Music Limited

Amazing Grace

This arrangement © Copyright 2000 Chester Music Limited

Go Down, Moses

The second part is optional - the melody can be sung in unison.

1. When Is - rael was in E - gypt's land, / saith the Lord, bold Mo - ses saith, / Let my peo - ple go!___ { Op - { If

- pressed so hard they could not stand, / not I'll smite your first - born dead, / Let my peo - ple go!

Go down, Mo - ses, Way down in E - gypt's land.___ Tell___ ole

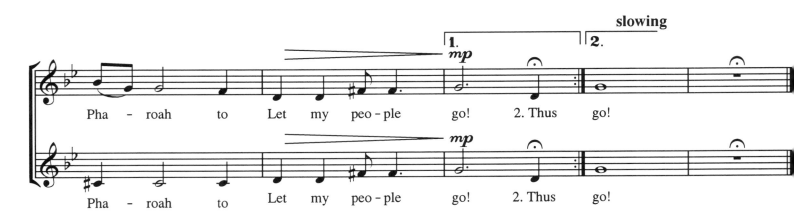

Pha - roah to Let my peo - ple go! 2. Thus go!

This arrangement © Copyright 2000 Chester Music Limited

Balm In Gilead

*To be sung second and third time round only.

This arrangement © Copyright 2000 Chester Music Limited

Good News!

This arrangement © Copyright 2000 Chester Music Limited

Deep River

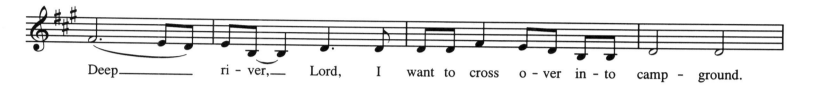

Deep_____ ri - ver,___ my home lies o - ver Jor - dan,

Deep_____ ri - ver,___ Lord, I want to cross o - ver in - to camp - ground.

Oh don't you want__ to go___ to that Gos - pel__ feast,___ That

pro - -mised__ land___ where all__ is peace.___ Deep___

ri - ver, my home is o - ver Jor - dan,_____ Deep_____

ri - ver, Lord, I want to cross o - ver in - to camp - ground._____

This arrangement © Copyright 2000 Chester Music Limited

Didn't My Lord Deliver Daniel?

This arrangement © Copyright 2000 Chester Music Limited

Nobody Knows De Trouble I See

Gently, slowly

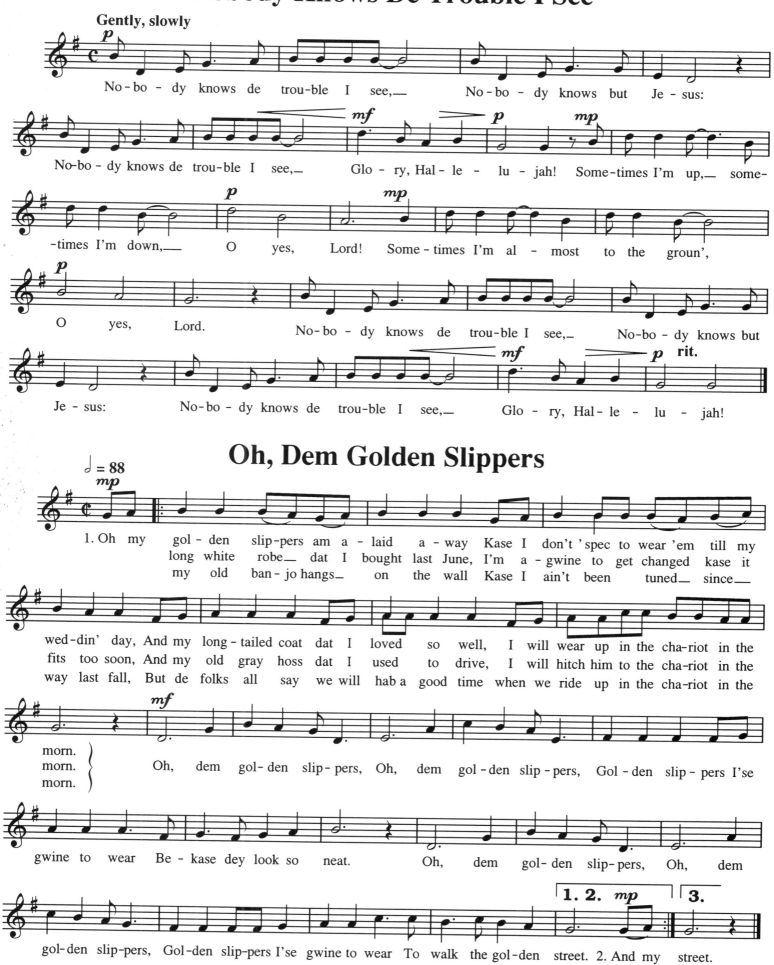

No-bo-dy knows de trou-ble I see,— No-bo-dy knows but Je-sus:

No-bo-dy knows de trou-ble I see,— Glo-ry, Hal-le-lu-jah! Some-times I'm up,— some-

-times I'm down,— O yes, Lord! Some-times I'm al-most to the groun',

O yes, Lord. No-bo-dy knows de trou-ble I see,— No-bo-dy knows but

Je-sus: No-bo-dy knows de trou-ble I see,— Glo-ry, Hal-le-lu-jah!

Oh, Dem Golden Slippers

♩ = 88

1. Oh my gol-den slip-pers am a-laid a-way Kase I don't 'spec to wear 'em till my
long white robe— dat I bought last June, I'm a-gwine to get changed kase it
my old ban-jo hangs— on the wall Kase I ain't been tuned— since—

wed-din' day, And my long-tailed coat dat I loved so well, I will wear up in the cha-riot in the
fits too soon, And my old gray hoss dat I used to drive, I will hitch him to the cha-riot in the
way last fall, But de folks all say we will hab a good time when we ride up in the cha-riot in the

morn.
morn.
morn. } Oh, dem gol-den slip-pers, Oh, dem gol-den slip-pers, Gol-den slip-pers I'se

gwine to wear Be-kase dey look so neat. Oh, dem gol-den slip-pers, Oh, dem

1. 2. *mp* 3.

gol-den slip-pers, Gol-den slip-pers I'se gwine to wear To walk the gol-den street. 2. And my street.
3. Oh—

This arrangement © Copyright 2000 Chester Music Limited

Roll, Jordan, Roll

There are various versions of this melody - this one is mine.

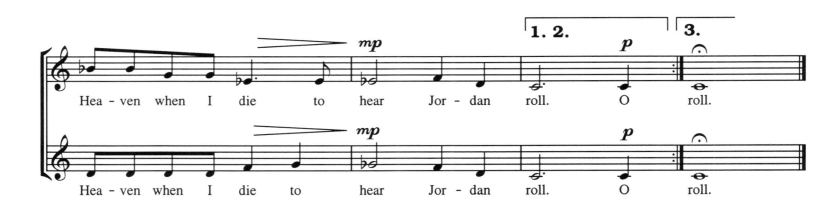

This arrangement © Copyright 2000 Chester Music Limited

Rock-a-my Soul

This arrangement © Copyright 2000 Chester Music Limited

Sometimes I Feel Like A Motherless Child

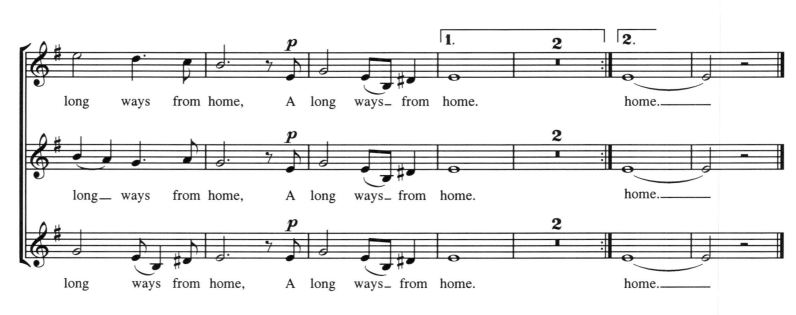

This arrangement © Copyright 2000 Chester Music Limited

Swing Low, Sweet Chariot

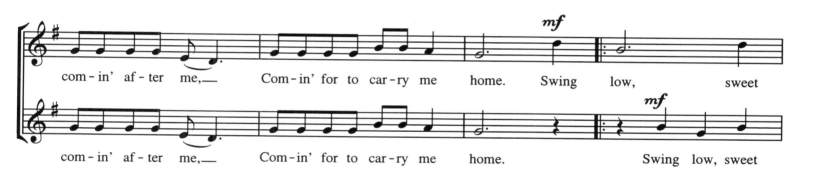

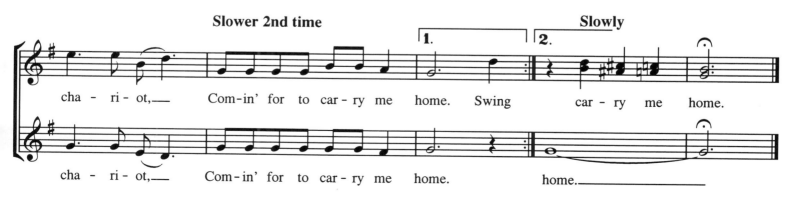

This arrangement © Copyright 2000 Chester Music Limited

Steal Away

Steal a - way, steal a - way, Steal a - way to Je - sus.

Steal a - way, steal a - way home, I ain't got long to stay here.

Green trees are bend - ing, Poor sin - ner stands a - trem - bling, The

trum - pet sounds with - in my soul, I ain't got long to stay here.

Green trees are bend - ing, Poor sin - ner stands a - trem - bling, The

trum - pet sounds with - in my soul, I ain't got long to stay here.

This arrangement © Copyright 2000 Chester Music Limited

This Train

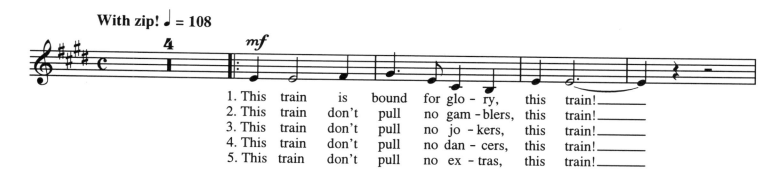

1. This train is bound for glo - ry, this train!_____
2. This train don't pull no gam - blers, this train!_____
3. This train don't pull no jo - kers, this train!_____
4. This train don't pull no dan - cers, this train!_____
5. This train don't pull no ex - tras, this train!_____

This train is bound for glo - ry, this train!_____   This train is
This train don't pull no gam - blers, this train!_____   This train don't
This train don't pull no jo - kers, this train!_____   This train don't
This train don't pull no dan - cers, this train!_____   This train don't
This train don't pull no ex - tras, this train!_____   This train don't

bound for glo - ry, if you ride it you must be ho - ly,
pull no gam - blers, nei - ther don't pull no mid - night ram - blers,
pull no jo - kers, ci - g'rette puf - fers and ci - gar smo - kers,
pull no dan - cers, hoo - chie-cootch sha - kers and Charles - ton pran - cers,
pull no ex - tras, don't pull no - thin' but the Heav'n - ly Spe - cial,

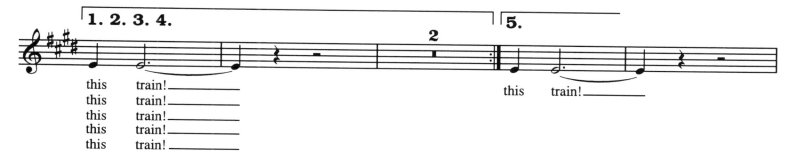

1. 2. 3. 4.   **5.**

this train!_____
this train!_____
this train!_____
this train!_____
this train!_____   this train!_____

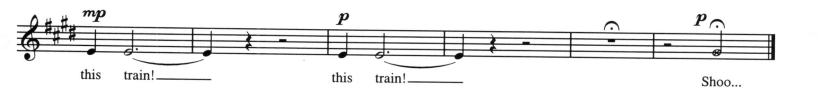

this train!_____   this train!_____   Shoo...

Try splitting the choir into two groups, one group making train noises alternating with the other group from verse 2 onwards, as follows:

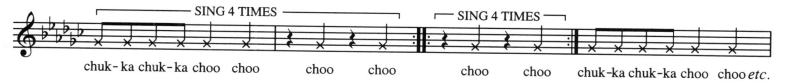

SING 4 TIMES   SING 4 TIMES

chuk-ka chuk-ka choo choo   choo   choo   choo   choo   chuk-ka chuk-ka choo choo *etc.*

This arrangement © Copyright 2000 Chester Music Limited

This World Is Not My Home

This is a perfect example of how the choice of key affects the colour and mood of a piece.
G♭ is the right key for this song in my opinion, but if you have difficulty with it, simply sing it in G.

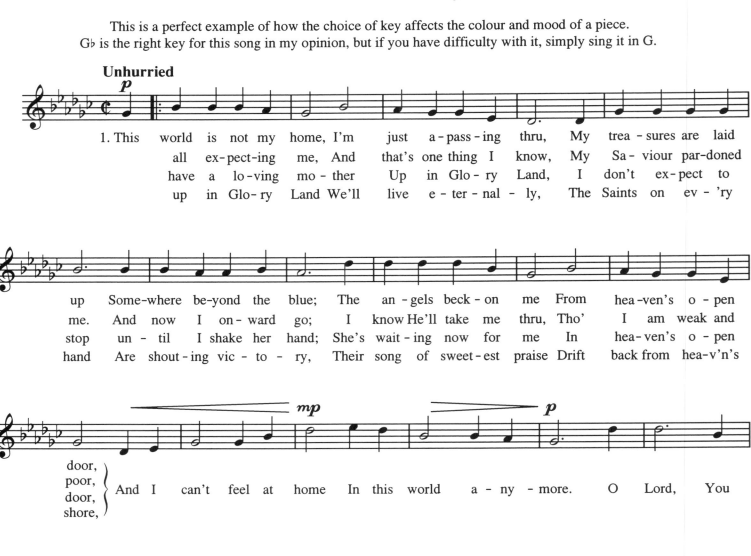

1. This world is not my home, I'm just a-pass-ing thru, My trea-sures are laid
all ex-pect-ing me, And that's one thing I know, My Sa-viour par-doned
have a lo-ving mo-ther Up in Glo-ry Land, I don't ex-pect to
up in Glo-ry Land We'll live e-ter-nal-ly, The Saints on ev-'ry

up Some-where be-yond the blue; The an-gels beck-on me From hea-ven's o-pen
me. And now I on-ward go; I know He'll take me thru, Tho' I am weak and
stop un-til I shake her hand; She's wait-ing now for me In hea-ven's o-pen
hand Are shout-ing vic-to-ry, Their song of sweet-est praise Drift back from hea-v'n's

door,
poor,
door,
shore, } And I can't feel at home In this world a-ny-more. O Lord, You

know I have no friend like you, If hea-ven's not my home, Then Lord, what will I

cresc.

do; The an-gels beck-on me From hea-ven's o-pen door, And I

1. 2. 3.   **4.**

can't feel at home In this world a-ny-more. {
2. They're
3. I   -more.
4. Just

This arrangement © Copyright 2000 Chester Music Limited

Walk In Jerusalem Just Like John

Steadily ♩ = c.126

mp

I want to be rea-dy, I want to be rea-dy,— I want to be rea-dy to

walk in Je-ru-sa-lem just like John. { John said the ci-ty was just four square,
Oh John, Oh John, What do you say? }

Walk in Je-ru-sa-lem just like John, { And he de-clared he'd meet me there,
That I'll be there in the com-ing day, }

mf

Walk in Je-ru-sa-lem just like John. I want to be rea-dy, I want to be

rea-dy,— I want to be rea-dy to walk in Je-ru-sa-lem just like John. When

dim.

Pe-ter was prea-ching at Pen-te-cost, Walk in Je-ru-sa-lem just like John, He

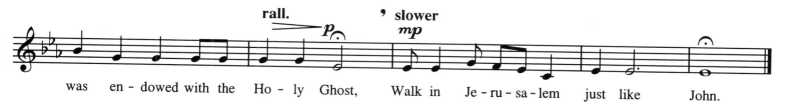

rall. *p* **' slower** *mp*

was en-dowed with the Ho-ly Ghost, Walk in Je-ru-sa-lem just like John.

This arrangement © Copyright 2000 Chester Music Limited

Were You There?

The part-singing is optional - the melody may be sung in unison throughout.

This arrangement © Copyright 2000 Chester Music Limited

When The Saints Go Marching In

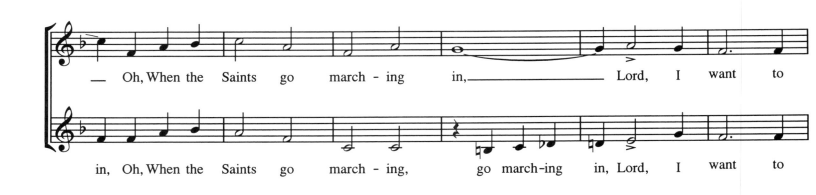

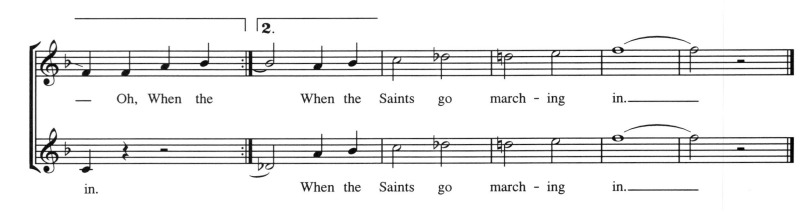

This arrangement © Copyright 2000 Chester Music Limited

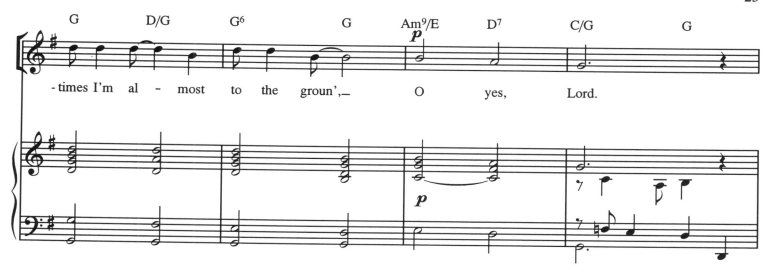

-times I'm al - most to the groun',— O yes, Lord.

No - bo - dy knows de trou - ble I see,— No - bo - dy knows but Je - sus:

No - bo - dy knows de trou - ble I see,— Glo - ry, Hal - le - lu - - jah!

Oh, Dem Golden Slippers

This arrangement © Copyright 2000 Chester Music Limited

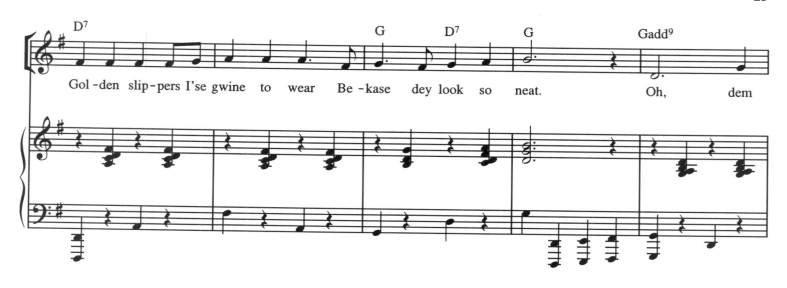

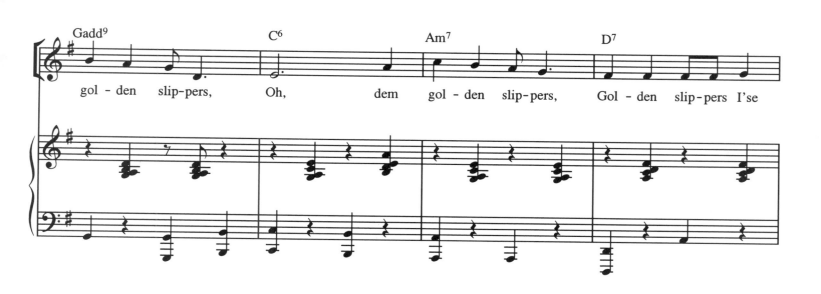

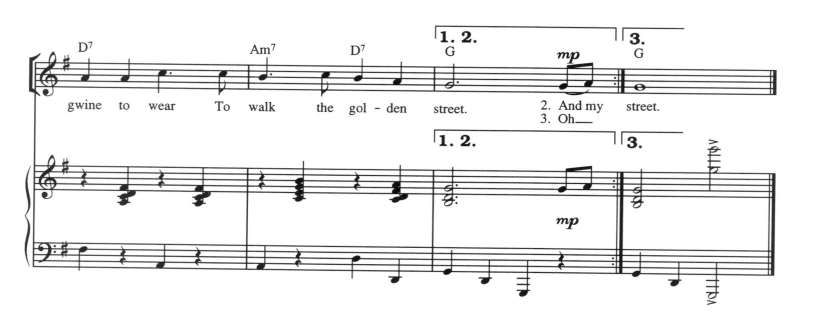

Roll, Jordan, Roll

There are various versions of this melody – this one is mine.

This arrangement © Copyright 2000 Chester Music Limited

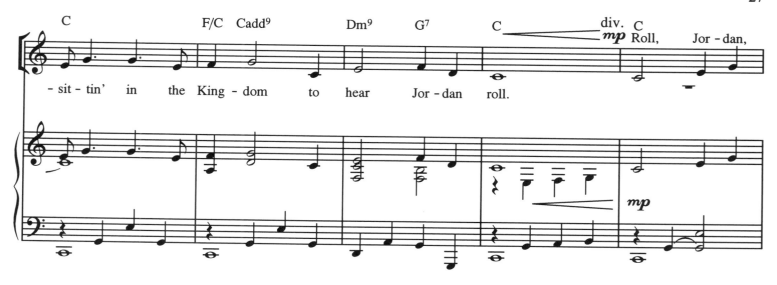

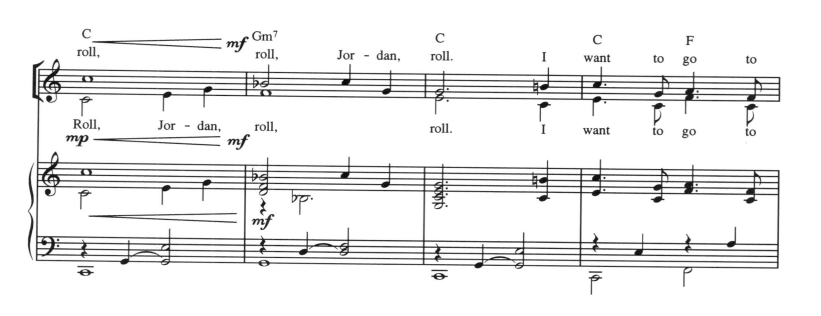

Rock-a-my Soul

This arrangement © Copyright 2000 Chester Music Limited

Sometimes I Feel Like A Motherless Child

This arrangement © Copyright 2000 Chester Music Limited

Swing Low, Sweet Chariot

* These are not heavy accents - think of them as emphasis rather than accent.

This arrangement © Copyright 2000 Chester Music Limited

Steal Away

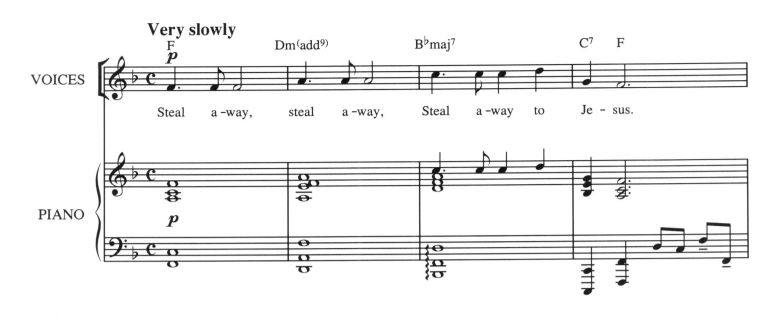

Steal a-way, steal a-way, Steal a-way to Je - sus.

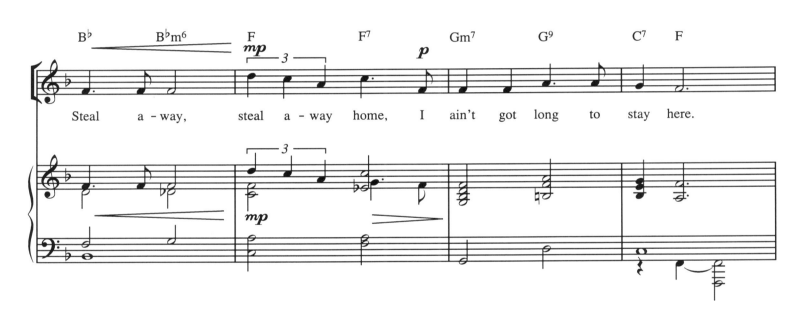

Steal a-way, steal a-way home, I ain't got long to stay here.

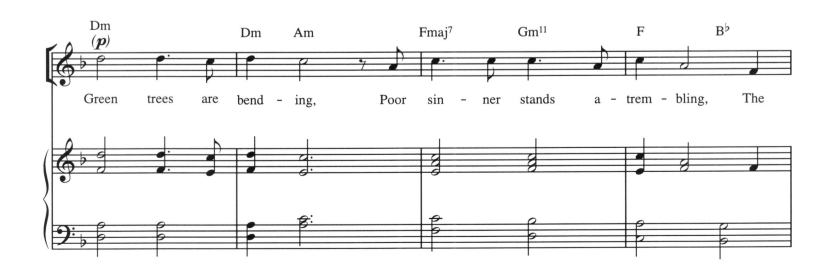

Green trees are bend-ing, Poor sin-ner stands a-trem-bling, The

This arrangement © Copyright 2000 Chester Music Limited

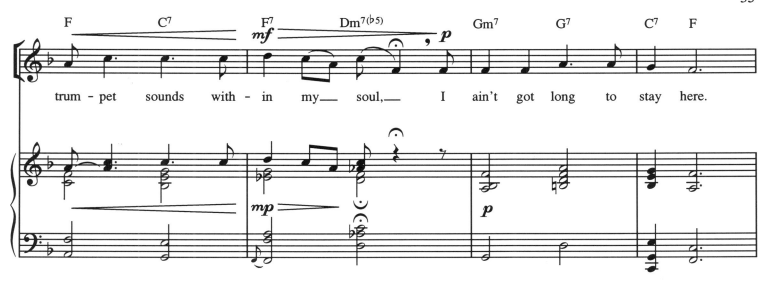

trum - pet sounds with - in my__ soul,__ I ain't got long to stay here.

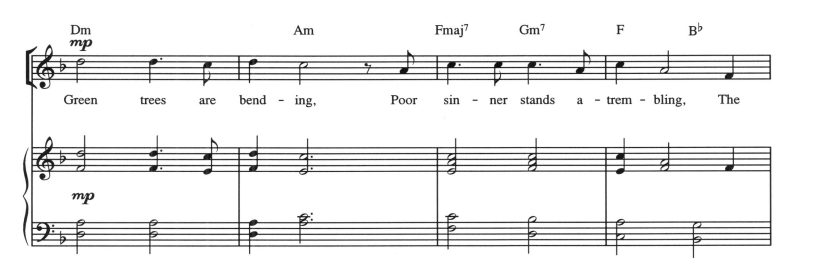

Green trees are bend - ing, Poor sin - ner stands a - trem - bling, The

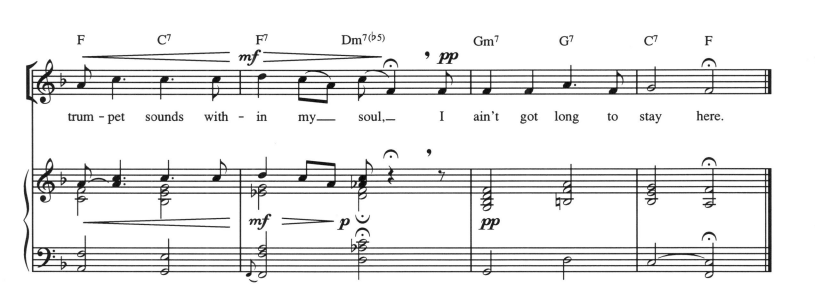

trum - pet sounds with - in my__ soul,__ I ain't got long to stay here.

This Train

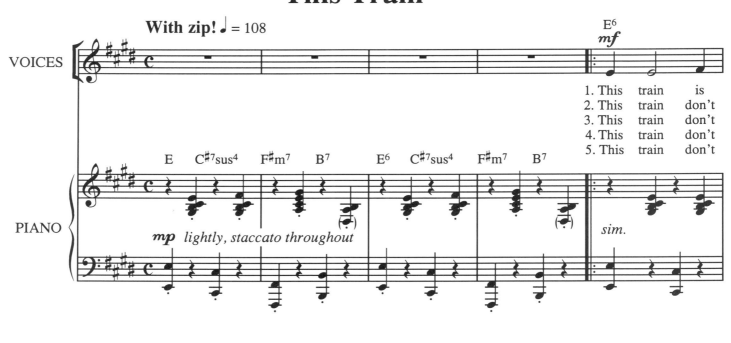

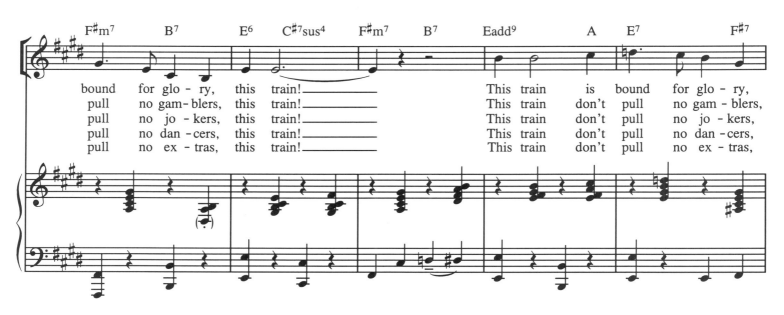

This arrangement © Copyright 2000 Chester Music Limited

Try splitting the choir into 2 groups, one group making train noises
alternating with the other group from verse 2 onwards, as follows:

SING 4 TIMES · SING 4 TIMES

chuk-ka chuk-ka choo choo · · choo · · choo · · choo · · choo · · chuk-ka chuk-ka choo choo *etc.*

This World Is Not My Home

This is a perfect example of how the choice of key affects the colour and mood of a piece.
G♭ is the right key for this song in my opinion, but if you have difficulty with it,
simply play it in G – any naturals become sharps and flats become naturals.

This arrangement © Copyright 2000 Chester Music Limited

-more. O Lord, You know I have no friend like you, If hea-ven's not my

home, Then Lord, what will I do; The an-gels beck-on me From hea-ven's o-pen

door, And I can't feel at home In this world a-ny-more.
2. They're
3. I -more.
4. Just

Walk In Jerusalem Just Like John

This arrangement © Copyright 2000 Chester Music Limited

* If everyone's feeling brave, use this harmony for verse 3, otherwise use the original version again.

Were You There?

The part-singing is optional – the melody can be sung in unison throughout.

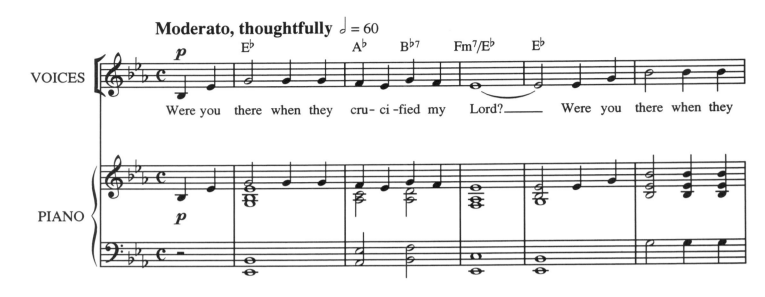

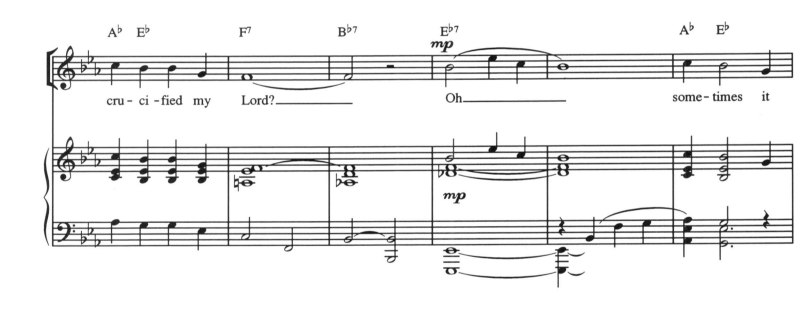

This arrangement © Copyright 2000 Chester Music Limited

When The Saints Go Marching In

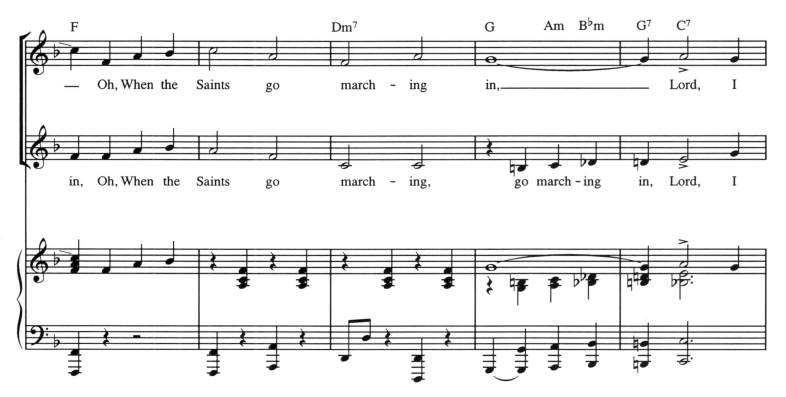

This arrangement © Copyright 2000 Chester Music Limited